Richard Scarry's
First Little Learners

This is
My House

It has
a roof.

It has windows.

It has a
backdoor.

6

It has
a chimney.

THIS IS MY HOUSE.

This is my angry
brother.

It has
a terrace.

It has a front door.

It has a
porch.

our
mailbox

lantern

7

THIS IS THE KITCHEN.

Mommy is cooking breakfast.

Catch!

window

pipe

clock

flying egg

coffee pot

spatula

pan

Mommy

refrigerator

egg box

eggshells

grater

ladle

bottle opener

rolling pin

table

whisk

pot

pan

handrail

flying toast

pitcher

teapot

creamer

toaster

staircase

plate

fork

knife

glass

salt and pepper

chair

stool

spoon

tablecloth

jam

9

THIS IS THE LIVING ROOM.

Daddy is going to work.
Don't be late!

window

curtain roc

priceless
painting

curtains

lamp

candle

candlestick

armchair

antenna

chess game

table

television
set

books

rug

another priceless painting

front door

paintbrush
and
paintbucket

keys

Daddy

steps

THIS IS THE BEDROOM.

piggy bank

lamp

chest of drawers

sleepy brother

blanket

stairwell

slippers

toy chest

pillow

noisy
sister

closet

window

bedside
table

rug

unmade bed

noisy
brother

Hey! Who forgot
to make his bed?

13

small window

THIS IS THE BATHROOM.

shower

shower-curtain rod

shower curtain

faucet

bathtub

sponge

puddles

bathmat

towel

towel rack

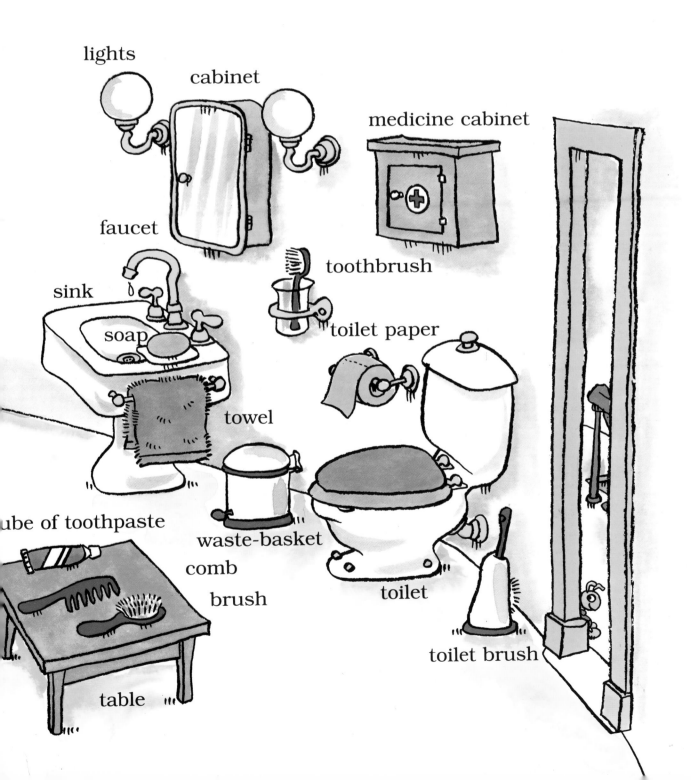

lights

cabinet

medicine cabinet

faucet

toothbrush

sink

soap

toilet paper

towel

ube of toothpaste

waste-basket

comb

brush

toilet

toilet brush

table

THE BASEMENT IS BENEATH THE HOUSE.

lamp

light switch

handrail

fuse box

Never, never touch!

stairway

electric plug

bucket

mat

mop

brush

washing machine

detergent

laundry basket

vase of flowers

THIS IS MOMMY'S STUDY.

radio

bookcase

window

Hello!

typewriter

curtains

writing paper

a ringing telephone

chair

dictionary

fire extinguisher

water heater

furnace

17

THE ATTIC IS UNDER THE ROOF.

carpenter

hammer

ladder

nail

shingles

new shingles

dusty attic

old scooter

18

A mason building the chimney.

trowel

bricks

roof

old lamp

old sewing machine

old kite

old roller skates

old wheel

gutter

19

WHERE DO YOU LIVE?
WHERE WOULD YOU LIKE TO LIVE?

water tower

In a cozy wooden chalet?

In an igloo made of ice?

taxi

In a tall apartment house?

laundry

In a houseboat?

thatched roof

In a cottage?

rope ladder

In a tree house?

In a wood-frame house?

garage